Creaking down the corridor

Poems Poems by David Harmer
Illustrated by Paul Cookson

1996

CREAKING DOWN THE CORRIDOR

First published August 1993 by
"A Twist In The Tale"
P.O. Box 25, Retford, Notts, DN22 7ER
2nd edition published April 1996

ISBN 1 874335 05 2

All poems written by David Harmer

All illustration artwork and layout by Paul Cookson

The poem "Picnic Poem" was first broadcast on BBC Verse Universe

The poems "Nowthen Davos" "The Ferret Poem" "Eulogy To Pontefract" and " North Sea Bathing" were first broadcast on "The Afternoon Shift" BBC Radio 4.

"The Picnic Poem" "Michael Hankie" and "Now Then Davos" also appear in "Now Then Davos" "A Twist In The Tale" 1990.

"Computer Closedown" was first published in "Techno Talk" Bodley Head, edited by Trevor Harvey 1994.

"Night Out With Gaz" was first published in "Disturbed Ground" by David Harmer published by Littlewood Press 1987

Thanks to Paul and Sally

Printed by:
Herbert Robinson
Elizabeth Court, Manners Industrial Estate,
Ilkeston, Derbyshire, Tel: 0115 944 2063

Contents

Dedicated to Paula

MISTER MOORE

Mister Moore Mister Moore
Creaking down the corridor

Uh ee Uh Uh ee
Uh ee Uh Uh ee

Mister Moore wears wooden suits
Mister Moore's got iron boots
Mister Moore's got hair like a brush
And Mister Moore don't like me much

Mister Moore Mister Moore
Creaking down the corridor

Uh ee Uh Uh ee
Uh ee Uh Uh ee

When my teacher's there I haven't got a care
Can do my sums, can do gerzinters
When Mister Moore comes through the door
Got a wooden head filled with splinters

Mister Moore Mister Moore
Creaking down the corridor

Uh ee Uh Uh ee
Uh ee Uh Uh ee

Mister Moore I implore
My ear holes ache, my head is sore
Don't come through that classroom door
Don't come through that classroom door

Mister Moore wears wooden suits
Mister Moore's got iron boots
Mister Moore's got hair like a brush
And Mister Moore don't like me much

Mister Moore Mister Moore
Creaking down the corridor

Uh ee Uh Uh ee
Uh ee Uh Uh ee

MICHAEL HANKIE

Well his name was Michael Hankie
And he came from Crystal Palace
And he wasn't a very nice boy.
At Alexandra Road Junior School
He nicked my favourite toy
But I didn't mind, I soon forgave him
Kept my temper believe it or not
Coz I realised the poor boy had a problem
His last name was covered in snot ! Yuk !

THERE'S VERY LITTLE MERIT IN A FERRET

There's very little merit in a ferret
Whipping up your trouser leg
Very little merit in ferret
Whipping up your trouser leg

If it were a pine martin
Oh boy you'd be smarting
If it were a puma you'd be dead

There's very little merit in a ferret
Whipping up your trouser leg

So if you dote on a stoat
If your heart goes blink for a mink
If you play footloose
With a mongoose
If you potter with an otter
If your beazel with a weasel
If your heart is set
On a marmoset
Then think

There's very little merit in a ferret
Whipping up your trouser leg

Ferret stoats they are vermin
You don't want your underpants
Trimmed with ermine

There's very little merit in a ferret
Whipping up your trouser leg

*PS When I wrote this poem I made a mistake. I thought a marmoset was
a type of ferret-like creature. It isn't. It's a small monkey. I meant a
marmot .. which of course is a small type of Bovril.*

4

SLUGS

Every morning
every night
I squeeze a squidge
of toothpaste on my brush.

It looks like a slug
a long, pink, shiny slug.

Close my eyes
shove it in my mouth
rub and scrub
up and down.

Squash it flat
against my teeth.

It tastes lovely
like a mint
the best slug
I've ever eaten.

Better than
the one I had yesterday
from the garden.

PASTING PATSY'S POSTERS

Petra Porter pastes in precincts
Patsy's pasty pasties posters
Patsy's posters for her pasties
And her tasty pastry pasta.

Patsy pays a pretty penny
For Petra's posters in her precincts
But Paula pastes her posters faster
Passes Petra, pasting past her.

So Patsy's posting Paula's posters
Paying pasty Paula plenty
For faster pasta poster pasting
Pasting pasta posters faster.

HARRY HOBGOBLIN'S SUPERSTORE

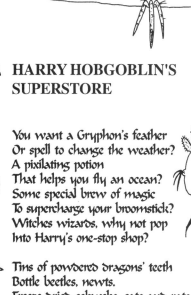

You want a Gryphon's feather
Or spell to change the weather?
A pixilating potion
That helps you fly an ocean?
Some special brew of magic
To supercharge your broomstick?
Witches wizards, why not pop
Into Harry's one-stop shop?

Tins of powdered dragons' teeth
Bottle beetles, newts.
Freeze-dried cobwebs, cats and rats
Screaming mandrake roots.
Lizard skins stirred widdershins
A Giant's big toe nail
Second hand spells used only once
New ones that can't fail.
Spells to grow some donkey's ears
On the teacher no-one likes
Spells to make you good at sums
Spells to find lost bikes.

Spells that grow
And stretch and shrink
Spells that make
Your best friend stink
Stacks of spells
Stacked on my shelves
Come on in, see for yourselves
Magic prices, bargains galore
At Harry Hobgoblin's Superstore.

THE VISITOR

It was late last night I'm certain
wasn't it
that I saw my bedroom curtain
twitch and flutter
fell a chill heard him mutter
"Hello lad I'm back"

Uncle Jack
dead since this night last year
wasn't it
a pickled onion in his beer
stopped his breath a sudden death
that took us sadly by surprise.

But there he was those eyes
one grey, one blue
one through
which the light could pass
the other, glass.

He drifted down, swam about
didn't he
in his brown suit, flat cap, stout
boots and tie
I saw him remove his eye
didn't I?

'It's not a dream
this' he said 'don't scream,
I'll not come back, I shan't return'
then I felt the ice cold burn
of his glass eye upon my skin.

Saw his ghastly ghostly grin
'Don't worry, don't get in a stew
just thought I'd keep an eye on you'

When I woke up today
I saw the blue eye not the grey
but when I picked it up to go
it drained away like melting snow.
Didn't it?

NOW THEN DAVOS

Well I went to buy a car, yes I went to buy a car
I went to buy a car in Doncaster
He got a chip stain on his breath
And a beer stain on his coat
He took me by the hand
And he shook me by the throat.

HE SAID
NOW THEN DAVOS
NOW THEN DAVOS
NOW THEN DAVOS
DOES THA LIVE IN A COMMUNE?

Oh what a greasy man
Oh what a greasy man
I saw him coming over
I nearly ran
He said is that the wife then?
Rubbed his slimy gut
Grabbed her by the chin
Said Nowthen Gingernut!

NOW THEN DAVOS ... etc.

Well you don't want a Fiat
You don't want a yellow car
You don't want front wheel drive
Haven't stood the test of time.
What you want's an Escort
Maybe red or black
And it just so happens pal
I've got one round the back.

NOW THE DAVOS ... etc.

Well we didn't buy a car
No we didn't buy a car
We didn't buy a car
From him in Doncaster
We ran to the bus stop
Glad to be alive
And we got a yellow Fiat
With front wheel drive.

NO THEN DAVOS ... etc.

NORTH SEA BATHING

The dash to the splash
Cuts short with the thought
Of the cold and the ice
Clamped like vice
You shiver, you moan
Chilled to the bone
By the freezing seas
Seizing your knees
In the absence of heat
You soon lose your feet
Arms flailing and lunging
You suddenly plunge in.

Quick quick do the underwater shuffle
You haven't got a sweater on, haven't got a duffle
Coat or long johns or donkey jacket
You shout and gibber, make a terrible racket
You thrash through the waves, struggle and kick
Mouthfuls of North Sea making you sick
You're blue and you're red, purple and glowing
Might get exposure so you'd better keep going
Do the underwater boogie, the keep alive jive
Headbutt an ice-berg with accidental dive
Frosts fill your face, a polar bear
Swims past your left leg, glares a hungry stare
Can't catch your breath, can't yell or shout
Without a doubt it's time to clamber out.

You dither and shiver
As you trot to the spot
Where your jeans and your woolly
Are completely buried in sand
The depth of your hand
Rough grit on your skin
Your teeth chattering

Your hair spiked and stiff
In a mad shipwrecked quiff
Despite all the pain
You'll be swimming again
Mad as a hatter
In subzero water
Though you're red and you're raw
It's what holidays are for.

TOO MUCH

My sister said "Let's try a new diet"
I said "Yes"

"Good for you food, no crisps or sweets"
I said "Yes"

That day we ate;
apples and pears,
plums and prunes
satsumas, bananas,
cherries and grapes
oranges, strawberries
figs and dates.

My sister said "My tummy hurts"
I said "Yes"

"Too much good-for-you-food
is bad-for-you-food.
I said "Yes"

"Shall we have a bag of sweets?"
And I said "Yes"

WHEN THE FURNITURE IS HUNGRY

Last night
Our armchair swallowed Dad
Just ate him up whole
In one big bite.

He was watching the football
United scored
Dad leaped in the air
Landed with a thump
And vanished.

I wasn't surprised.
Last week the settee
Gobbled down Grandma
As she did her knitting
And moaned at the weatherman.

'Rain again' she grumbled
In a gulp she was gone
Making the cushions all lumpy.

Mum thinks
Its time we had
A new three piece suite.

We hope it will be a vegetarian.

SNAPSHOTS

The Christmas when
Auntie Joan tripped on the cat
and landed nose-first in its dinner

and uncle Jack walked at midnight
through deep snow chasing pixies
to help them count the stars

and Grandma Higgins lost her teeth
at the bottom of the pudding
fishing for sixpences

was the Christmas I got a train set
and fused all the lights up my street
when I plugged it in.

The summer beach
where Jane and I buried Nathaniel
our hated cousin as he lay sunbathing

And uncle Jack and Auntie Joan
were sick after their roller coaster
whisked up their fish and chips and
pale ale

and Grandma Higgins
fell fast asleep on her lilo
drifted out past the lighthouse

snoring like a dozing walrus
she was rescued by a trawler
who mistook her for a whale.

And that one's of my feet and that
is of my thumb, and that's my mum
except you can't see her head.

I'll paste them up and stick them in
after all it's only once
you'll get a set snaps like these.

Shall we look at them again?

A PARCEL OF BIRDS

Sky-high
the grey gulls fly
swoop and tumble.

Above the crow
flapping low across the field
to the trees.

Where busy sparrows
dart and flick, quick as arrows
they fuss and chatter.

Starlings scatter
in a noisy flock of squabbles
fight and troubles.

Stiff on stilts
the heron struts down his stream
a blackbird sings.

Nightfall brings
the slow silent beat of wings
as the owl.

Drops like snow
on the mouse, or shrew, or vole
squeaking below.

ONCE THERE WERE ELEPHANTS

Whose grey ghost have I seen
slowly drift across the plains
like the shadow of a mountain?

Which wild cry did I hear
fade to dust in the empty valleys
filled with rock?

Which mighty heart did I feel
pound and dance like a fierce drum
then echo into silence?

Which dreadful death have I tasted
under blazing skies, where are the sheds
stacked high with ivory?

When will the rolling herds return
often they took days to pass
churning the earth with their thunder?

When will some real answers
be shouted across the world
loud enough for us to listen?

LET'S GO STEELERS LET'S GO

LET'S GO STEELERS LET'S GO

Rocket Ron hits the ice
He cuts up rough, none too nice

At number ten trouble's brewing
Storming Steve leaves them a ruin

Slams that stick, a powerplay
Blows the other team away

LET'S GO STEELERS LET'S GO

Down the rink, in the groove
You should see those steelers move

Sharp as lightening, fierce as thunder
Watch that other team go under

Ten more goals hit the slot
The ice is cold but the Steelers are not

LET'S GO STEELERS LET'S GO

ROCKET RON!
STEELERS OO OO
ROCKET RON!
STEELERS OO OO
ROCKET RON!
STEELERS OO OO

LET'S GO STEELERS LET'S GO

We defeat so many teams
Freezing up their hopes and dreams

Give them all such a belting
Move so fast the ice is melting

Start off tall, but they end up sore
None of these came back for more

The Retford Rotters and the Sprotbrough Slugs
The Wigan Winkles and the Bedford Bugs
The Barnsley Bottoms and the Scarborough Slackers
The Luton Loafers and the Crew Cream Crackers
The Dudley Duds and the Salisbury Sillies
The Nuneaton Nutters and the Wellington Willies
The Greasborough Greasers and the Shrewsbury Shews
They all get the losing-to-the-mighty-Steelers-blues

LET'S GO STEELERS LET'S GO

NIGHTS OUT WITH GAZ

A night out with Gaz
was over the wall
and into a big castle
bigger than Camelot.

The tower burned
silver with moonlight,
we'd sit in the arch
of a window talking.

Then back to his house
for mystery tins
bought cheap with no labels
by his mum from the market.

Two mugs of tea
and beans on toast
or maybe rice pudding
prunes or dog meat.

Next morning with Mick
we'd deliver the papers
the man in the shop
thought we were daft.

"You ought to grow up
not make stupid noises
in the castle at midnight
lads of your age."

I'd think of that tower
pale as a ghost ship
silence hanging
like mist round the mast.

Why grow up
and have to leave Camelot;
why always know
that this time its beans?

A HOT TIME IN THE SUPERMARKET

When my mum gave my dad
The juiciest, most romantic kiss
Right there in the supermarket.

And worse
Began to quickstep him down the aisle
To their favourite tune.

I couldn't believe it.
Everybody stared.
My cheeks began to burn.

In our basket
The hot-chilli sauce sweated
Ice-cream melted
Ten frozen fishfingers defrosted
The fizzy wine popped its cork
The tomato sauce went redder
The tinned salmon pinker
The cream of mushroom soup
Boiled over
And the chicken drumsticks
Beat out a tango.

I had to have
Three tins of pop from the cold shelf
Two ice-lollies
And a big swig of natural water
Just to get over it.

TRAGIC MAGIC

Round the back of the Big Toy Shop
They've put a giant skip
Full of duff and broken stuff
They're dumping at the tip.

It's where I found a magic set
With Mark the other day
The box was broken, some bits were lost
But the wand was still ok.

I said to Mark 'Wish you're a horse'
I was only playing
Next thing I knew he'd galloped off
Round the car park neighing.

I wished him back, then wished I was
A footballer millionaire
We wished for pop and sweets and cakes
And suddenly they were there.

I wanted most and so did Mark
He pulled my hair, I called him names
We had a fight and fell out
No more playing games.

'I wish I'd never seen this thing'
I cried and off it flew
So just watch out if you find the wand
It will do the same to you.

COMPUTER CLOSEDOWN

I clicked on the mouse
and the mouse began to squeak
it had nested in the disk-drive
been hiding there all week
so it flicked its plastic whiskers
shook its plastic head
wrote GET LOST on the monitor
PICK ON SOMEONE ELSE INSTEAD.

I programmed the turtle
and the turtle was annoyed
he'd been swimming in the school pool
but now became employed
in spinning round the classroom
until it hurt its head
he commanded the monitor
PICK ON SOMEONE ELSE INSTEAD.

The monitor was angry
she's been giving out the ink
now these computer creatures
were trying to make her think
she'd been butted by the RAM
and the cursor called her names
so she closed down all the systems
and blew up all the games.

She sat there with grey face
a square and silent head
the printer typed her last words
PICK ON SOMEONE ELSE INSTEAD.

THE KITCHEN TAP DISASTER

The kitchen tap is dripping
My dad sent for the plumber
It's pouring out in a flood
Won't get any slower.

DRIP DRIP DRIPPERTY DRIP
DRIP DRIP DRIPPERTY DRIP

The kitchen tap is dripping
Dad says it needs a washer
Mum is getting furious
Says dad should have a spanner.

DRIP DRIP ... etc.

The kitchen tap is dripping
And floating on the water
Are all the kitchen pots and pans
And my baby brother

DRIP DRIP ... etc.

The kitchen tap is dripping
But dad's a splendid swimmer
He's pumping up the dinghy
As he snorkels in the larder.

DRIP DRIP ... etc.

The kitchen tap's stopped dripping
A frogman and a diver
Have arrived to mend the pipes
I'll just switch on the shower ...

DRIP DRIP DRIPPERTY DRIP
DRIP DRIP DRIPPERTY DRIP

PICNIC POEM

In our car in our car
In our c-c-car
In our car in our car
In our wonderful car

We're up and away it's a beautiful day
Zooming along down the main highway
Dad at the wheel picnic in the boot
Sunlight and laughter planning the route.

In our car in our car
In our c-c-car
In our car in our car
In our wonderful car

Crunch bang, What's that?
Crunch bang, What's that?
A whistle and a knock, a thumping shock
A whining fizz and a crack on the block
A rattle and splutter, a groaning mutter
Cuts through the racket like a knife through butter.

That's our car that's our car
That's our wonderful car
That's our car that's our car
That's our Shhhhhhhhhhhhhh

Crunch bang. What's that?
Crunch bang. What's that?
A shove and a kick, dad's got a stick
And he's banging on the engine cos it makes him sick
A mallet and a crowbar, to try to make it go far
He'd be better off trying to drive my Granny's sofa

We've stopped, we're stuck, we're out of luck
Waiting for the man with the breakdown truck
Out with the picnic up with the bonnet
We'll be stuck here for hours you can bet your life upon it

In our car in our car
In our c-c-car
In our car in our car
In our useless car

I HATE GARDENING

Oh, I have walked though gardens
From Sissinghurst to Kew
From Hidcote down to Barnsley
I've seen a bloom or two
But I'm not deceived
By green Arcadian bowers
Some poor clot
Has dug the lot
And it took him hours.

Me, I killed my sweet peas
Likewise my hollyhocks
I had badly drooping lupins
Bankrupted all my stocks
I had failures with my dahlias
My roses died and withered
My daffodils were very ill
My buzzie lizzies dithered.

Yes I have walked through gardens
From Tintinhull to Roundhay
With the ghost of Gertrude Jekyll
Hearing what the grounds say
They whisper in my ear
Of sylvern nymph-filled acres
But some poor bod
Raised every clod
Then met the undertakers.

In my imagination
There lies a perfect garden
Most of it is concrete
I watch it set and harden
But in the bit that's muddy
Are planted bright Spring borders
And some poor jerk is hard at work
And it's me that's giving orders.

JACK'S MAGIC SET

'It really will work' said Jack yesterday
Just as our teacher was clearing away
'If I wave this wand and say the right words
That pile of maths books will turn into birds.'

Chalk powdered our hair, ink squirted our faces
The rulers and pencils began to run races
Our teacher became a most elegant pig
Waving his trotters and dancing a jig.

'I've got it for Christmas from my Uncle Stan
Such an amazing, mysterious man
He wears a long cloak, a tall pointed hat
A wizard of course, no doubt about that.'

Our Headmaster was starting to shout
As giant erasures were rubbing him out
Miss Brown grew a beard, Miss Green turned red
With the caretaker's mop stuck on her head.

The school went so crazy it gave us a fright
But Jack's Uncle Stan made everything right
Except for one thing, a real disaster
He could not seem to return our headmaster.

US COOL CATZ FEATURING MC SPATZ: MIAOW 2 MIAOW

Spats and Tabby and Pete
Giving it some whatfor down in the street
Singing our heads off, high pitched howling
Growling, scowling, hissing and yowling.

We're the cat choir, the real cool crew
Every night everyone knows what we do
Baseball caps, rap and rave, eardrum reaching
Squealing, screaking, wailing and screeching.

We don't get paid, don't get applause
Just water on our heads and mud on our paws
Windows fly open, doors slam back
We get a lot of language, get a lot of flack
Nobody likes us, don't ask me why
As we open our furry throats and sing into the sky.

We're out in the dark, screaming at the stars
Busking under bushes, crooning under cars
Slinking over walls, creeping and crawling
Calling out our appalling caterwauling.

The sun comes up, the birds start to cheep
We think about breakfast, we think about sleep
Tomorrow we'll start again, it never stops
We'll bop till we drop on our Top of the Pops.

LITTLE LISA

Little Lisa likes to lick
lots and loads of lovely lollies
lime and lychees, melons, lemon,
lychees, lime and lemon, melon,
melon, lemon, lime and lychees,
lemon, melon, lychees, lime.

Licking lollies little Lisa
liked to lick Molly's lollies.
Licking lollies little Lisa
liked to lick Polly's lollies.
Licking lollies little Lisa
liked to lick Holly's lollies.
Molly's lollies, Polly's lollies,
Holly's lollies, jolly lollies
Lots and loads and loads and lots
and lots and loads and loads and lots
and lots of lovely jolly lollies
Little Lisa liked to lick.

Little Lisa liked to lick
lots of lovely jolly lollies
nicked the licks from Molly's lollies
nicked the licks from Polly's lollies
quickly licked Holly's lollies
quickly licked lots of lollies
lemon lollies
melon lollies
lime lollies
lots and lots of lovely lollies
Little Lisa liked to lick.

34

EULOGY TO PONTEFRACT

My sensations were high-jacked
Where toasted coconut also spracht
And toothsome odours filled the air
They lingered in my nostrils there
Bushwacked
By liquorice in Pontefract

At once my taste buds were attacked
Flatpacked, sacked and neatly stacked
To be tickled, pampered, ravished
As Pontefract cake on me were lavished
I cracked
And gorged myself in Pontefract.

Although I've kept my teeth intact
There was no sweetmeal that I lacked
As I chewed and chomped and munched
Ate no tea and seldom lunched
But snacked
More than somewhat in Pontefract.

I miss those tastes, those smells, in fact
More than once I have back-tracked
Sauntered down old Swanhill Lane
Sniffed the sugary air again
Ransacked
Nostalgia's dreams in Pontefract.

You miss the place once you have long gone
In this case I miss the bon-bons
You miss the byways, shops and streets
In this case I miss the sweets
You miss the parks and tennis courts
I mostly miss the liquorice allsorts
That's fact
Nowhere's as sweet as Pontefract.

THERE'S A MONSTER IN YOUR GARDEN

If the water in your fishpond fizzes and foams
And there's giant teeth-marks on the plastic gnomes
You've found huge claw-prints in the flower bed
And just caught sight of a two-horned head
Put a stick in your front lawn with a piece of card on
Look Out Everybody-There's A Monster In My Garden.

You haven't seen the dustman for several weeks
Not seen the gasman who was looking for leaks
Not seen the paper-girl, postman or plumber
Haven't seen the window cleaner since last summer
Don't mean to be nosey, I do beg your pardon
It seems to me there's a monster in your garden.

One dark night it will move in downstairs
Start living in the kitchen, take you unawares
Frighten you, bite on you, with howls and roars
It will crash and smash about, push you out of doors
In the cold and snow and rain the ice will harden
On you and your family shivering in the garden.

Now listen to me neighbour, all of this is true
It happened next door now it's happening to you
There's something nasty on the compost heap
Spends all day there curled up asleep
You don't want your bones crunched or jarred on
Just you watch out for the monster in your garden.

ALL OF US KNOCKING ON THE STABLE DOOR

Three great kings, three wise men
Tramp across the desert to Bethlehem
Arrive at the inn, don't travel no more
They start knocking at the stable door.

Knocking at the door, knocking at the door
All of us are knocking at the stable door.

I've got myrrh, he's got gold
He's got frankincense and all of us are cold
We stand here shivering, chilled to the core
We're just knocking on the stable door.

The star above it glows in the sky
Burning up the darkness and we know why
A baby King's asleep in the straw
So we start knocking on the stable door.

Travelled some distance, we've travelled far
Melchior, Casper and Balthazaar
We are so wealthy, the baby's so poor
But here we are knocking on the stable door.

Now is the time, now is the hour
To feel the glory, worship the power
We quietly enter, kneel on the floor
Just the other side of the stable door.

Knocking on the door, knocking on the door
All of us knocking at the stable door.

Knocking on the door, knocking on the door
We're all knocking at the stable door.

39

THE NEWS

I don't like news
that explodes
leaves refugees
crying, homeless

that orders tanks
into cities
blasting down
schools and houses.

News that blows up
hospitals
news that kills
and fills deep graves.

I don't like news
that screams abuse
kicks the legs
from under wingers.

taps their ankles
argues back
news that won't learn
how to lose.

I like news
that's just been born
news that puts
food in stomachs.

news that rescues
news that cures
that celebrates
its hundredth birthday

news that will make today
happier than the day before.

JACK-BY-THE-HEDGE

White flowers
Leaves so clean
Jack-by-the-hedge
Is tall and green.

Oily cars
Carbon smoke
Jack-by-the-hedge
Starts to choke.

A rusty pram
A broken bed
Jack-by-the-hedge
Bows his head.

Filthy air
Dirt on his coat
Jack-by-the-hedge
Has soot in his throat.

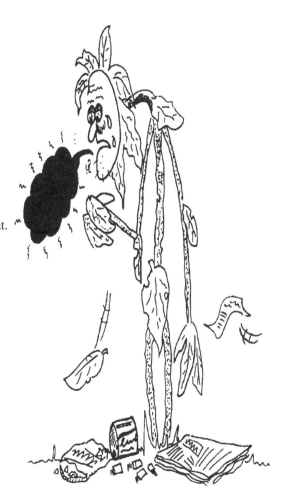

For over ten years DAVID HARMER has been performing, writing, telling stories, yelling poems, editing books and making people laugh. He has appeared in thousands of venues up and down the country, ranging from schools, folk-clubs, colleges, conferences, libraries, festivals and arts centres to fields, streets and someone's front room. He is an experienced workshop leader and has run a large number of In-service courses for teachers.

He has made many appearances on Radio and TV and was a founder member of the performance poetry group Circus Of Poets.

Now he works with Paul Cookson in the exciting and popular SPILL THE BEANS poetry duo.

He has had countless poems for children published in many anthologies as well as two books of stories. He has edited children's books and has four collections of poetry for adults in print. This is the first collection of poetry for children. He hopes you enjoy it. As he is a Primary School Headteacher in Doncaster, if you don't he'll keep you in at playtimes. So there!

SPILL THE BEANS

Paul Cookson and David Harmer

" In their unique performance
Spill The Beans brings out the child in
every adult and the adult in every child. "
Nick Toczek, Bradford Festival

David Harmer and Paul Cookson also work together as Spill The Beans - a performance poetry act for all the family.

A lively entertaining show can be guaranteed with laughs, high speed performance poetry and plenty of audience participation.

Together they have performed thousands of shows at thousands of venues.

As experienced teachers they have also organised hundreds of workshops for all ages as well as numerous In Service Courses and training for teachers, librarians and others.

For further information and bookings write (with S.A.E.) to :

Spill The Beans
P.O. Box 25
Retford
Notts DN22 7ER

BOOKS AVAILABLE FROM "A TWIST IN THE TALE"

Spill The Beans

Illustrated poems by
Paul Cookson & David Harmer
£3.95 (incl. p&p)

Big Red Undies

Greatest hits by
Paul Cookson & David Harmer
£1.99 (incl. p&p)

Let No-one Steal Your Dreams

Poems by
Paul Cookson
£4.95 (incl. p&p)

Over 21 And Still Into Noddy

Selected poems 1979 - 91
by Paul Cookson
Intro by Noddy Holder
£5.35 (incl. p&p)

Creaking Down The Corridor

Poems by David Harmer
Illustrated by Paul Cookson
£3.95 (incl. p&p)

Spill The Beans Badges

50p each (incl. p&p)

Captain Concorde Badges

50p each (incl. p&p)

AVAILABLE FROM SEPTEMBER 1st 1996

Secret Staffrooms And Crazy Classrooms

The Spill The Beans Guide
to Schools by Paul Cookson
and David Harmer
£3.95 (incl. p&p)

The Toilet Seat Has Teeth
New Edition containing poems from The Amazing
Captain Concorde, Happy As A Pig In Muck, The
Toilet Seat Has Teeth and Rhyming Rhythams For
Twisted Tongues

Illustrated poems by
Paul Cookson
£4.95 (incl. p&p)

Available from:
A TWIST IN THE TALE, P.O. BOX 25, RETFORD, NOTTS, DN22 7ER

Please make all cheques and postal orders payable to "A TWIST IN THE TALE"
Allow 28 days for delivery

ISBN: 978-1-0881-5882-1

BRUH! YOU GOT THIS
Affirmations for Young Men

Published by Verse One Enterprises
An imprint of E. Marcel Ministries

www.emarceljones.com

CONTENTS

BRUH, YOU GOT THIS!

The power of a strong affirmation is not to be underestimated. In fact, all you really need in order to start your path towards greatness is to be affirmed that you have what it takes to be successful. Bruh, you got this! So, begin your journey, today, and absorb every positive anecdote contained in this debut project by *Trevor Jones*.

THIS WEEK'S AFFIRMATION

I AM LOVED

John 3:16

For God loved the world so much
that he gave his only Son so that
anyone who believes in him shall
not perish but have eternal life.

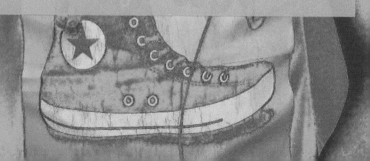

YOU ARE LOVED

WHAT'S ON YOUR MIND:

Who influences me the most? Why?

_____

_____

_____

_____

EVERY DAY THIS WEEK
- *Complete 5 pushups*
- *Complete 10 sit-ups*
- *Complete 20 jumping jacks*

TAKE ACTION

Take a selfie hugging someone that loves you

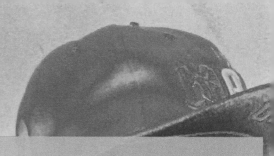

THIS WEEK'S AFFIRMATION

I AM RESPECTFUL

Matthew 7:12
Don't be selfish; don't live to make a good impression on others. Be humble, thinking of others as better than yourself.

YOU ARE RESPECTFUL

WHAT'S ON YOUR MIND:

What things would I like to change about myself?

_____

_____

_____

EVERY DAY THIS WEEK

- *Complete 5 pushups*
- *Complete 10 sit-ups*
- *Complete 20 jumping jacks*

TAKE ACTION

This week, maintain a respectful tone and demeanor when interacting with others

THIS WEEK'S AFFIRMATION

I AM
INTELLIGENT

Proverbs 18:15
The intelligent man is always open to new ideas. In fact, he looks for them.

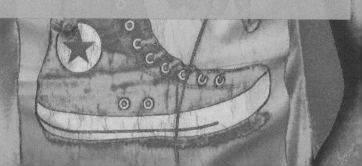

YOU ARE INTELLIGENT

WHAT'S ON YOUR MIND:

When I become an adult, I plan to have a career in...

_____

_____

EVERY DAY THIS WEEK

- Complete 10 pushups
- Complete 15 sit-ups
- Complete 25 jumping jacks

TAKE ACTION

Visit the library and check out a book on a subject about which you know very little

THIS WEEK'S AFFIRMATION

I AM STRONG

Joshua 1:9
Yes, be bold and strong! Banish
fear and doubt! For remember, the
Lord your God is with you
wherever you go.

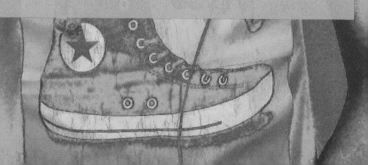

YOU ARE STRONG

WHAT'S ON YOUR MIND:

I am proud that I accomplished the following things:

_____

_____

_____

EVERY DAY THIS WEEK

- Complete 10 pushups
- Complete 15 sit-ups
- Complete 25 jumping jacks

TAKE ACTION

This week, add ten more pushups, ten more sit-ups, and ten more jumping jacks to your exercise routine

THIS WEEK'S AFFIRMATION

I AM WISE

Proverbs 19:20
Get all the advice you can and be
wise the rest of your life.

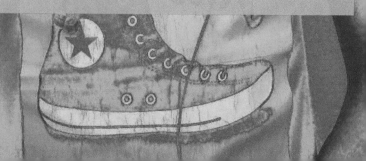

YOU ARE WISE

WHAT'S ON YOUR MIND:

I constantly dream about the following things:

_____

_____

_____

EVERY DAY THIS WEEK

- *Complete 15 pushups*
- *Complete 20 sit-ups*
- *Complete 30 jumping jacks*

TAKE ACTION

This week, before you make a major decision, make a list of pros and cons

THIS WEEK'S AFFIRMATION

I AM
COURAGEOUS

Proverbs 28:1
The wicked flee when no one is
chasing them! But the godly are
bold as lions!

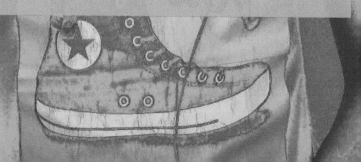

YOU ARE COURAGEOUS

WHAT'S ON YOUR MIND:

These three things frighten me the most.

_____

_____

_____

EVERY DAY THIS WEEK

- Complete 15 pushups
- Complete 20 sit-ups
- Complete 30 jumping jacks

TAKE ACTION

This week, challenge yourself to be more courageous when you speak

THIS WEEK'S AFFIRMATION

I AM NEEDED

Luke 12:7

And he knows the number of hairs on your head! Never fear, you are far more valuable to him than a whole flock of sparrows.

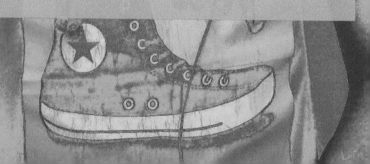

YOU ARE NEEDED

WHAT'S ON YOUR MIND:

Who encourages me the most?

_____

_____

_____

_____

EVERY DAY THIS WEEK

- Complete 20 pushups
- Complete 25 sit-ups
- Complete 35 jumping jacks

TAKE ACTION

This week, clean up an area of the house that has been neglected

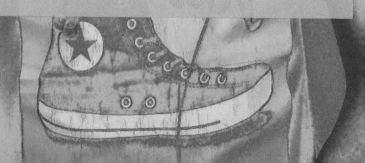

THIS WEEK'S AFFIRMATION

I AM DESERVING

Romans 5:8
But God showed his great love for us by sending Christ to die for us while we were still sinners.

YOU ARE DESERVING

WHAT'S ON YOUR MIND:

These three things make me smile. Why?

_____

_____

_____

EVERY DAY THIS WEEK

- *Complete 20 pushups*
- *Complete 25 sit-ups*
- *Complete 35 jumping jacks*

TAKE ACTION

This week, do something special for yourself (prepare your favorite meal, watch your favorite show, etc.)

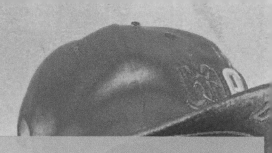

THIS WEEK'S AFFIRMATION

I AM NOBLE

Isaiah 32:8
But good men will be generous to
others and will be blessed of God
for all they do.

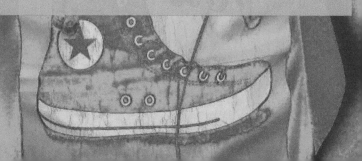

YOU ARE NOBLE

WHAT'S ON YOUR MIND:
The best sport ever created is... Why?

_____

_____

_____

_____

EVERY DAY THIS WEEK
•*Take a 20 minute walk around the neighborhood with an adult or friend*

TAKE ACTION
This week, help someone in need of a helping hand

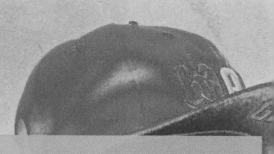

THIS WEEK'S AFFIRMATION

I AM PERSISTENT

Galatians 6:9

And let us not get tired of doing what is right, for after a while we will reap a harvest of blessing if we don't get discouraged and give up.

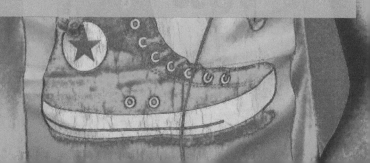

YOU ARE PERSISTENT

WHAT'S ON YOUR MIND:

What will my report card look like this period?

_____

_____

_____

_____

EVERY DAY THIS WEEK

•Take a 25 minute walk around the neighborhood with a friend or adult

TAKE ACTION

Challenge yourself to complete a project, assignment, or task

THIS WEEK'S AFFIRMATION

I AM RELIABLE

Titus 2:7

And you yourself must be an example to them of good deeds of every kind. Let everything you do reflect your love of the truth and the fact that you are in dead earnest about it.

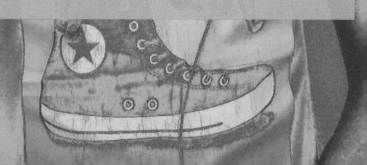

YOU ARE RELIABLE

WHAT'S ON YOUR MIND:

Who is my best friend?

_____

_____

_____

EVERY DAY THIS WEEK

•Take a 30 minute walk around the neighborhood with a friend or adult

TAKE ACTION

Volunteer to assist your teacher or parents with a project

THIS WEEK'S AFFIRMATION

I AM MADE IN GOD'S IMAGE

Genesis 39:6

So Potiphar gave Joseph the complete administrative responsibility over everything he owned. He hadn't a worry in the world with Joseph there, except to decide what he wanted to eat! Joseph, by the way, was a very handsome young man.

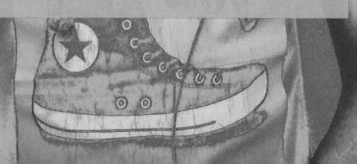

YOU ARE MADE IN GOD'S IMAGE

WHAT'S ON YOUR MIND:
What I love about my body is...

_____

_____

_____

EVERY DAY THIS WEEK
- *Hold a PLANK position for 10 seconds (complete twice)*

TAKE ACTION
Take a selfie that shows off your strong profile

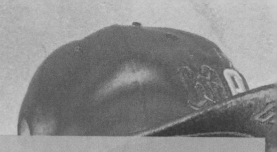

THIS WEEK'S AFFIRMATION

I AM ENOUGH

I Corinthians 6:19
Haven't you yet learned that your
body is the home of the Holy Spirit
God gave you, and that he lives
within you? Your own body does
not belong to you.

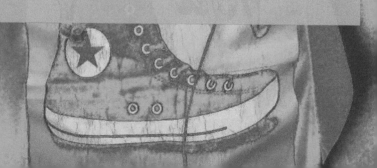

YOU ARE ENOUGH

WHAT'S ON YOUR MIND:

What motivates me to be great? Why?

_____

_____

_____

_____

EVERY DAY THIS WEEK

•Hold a PLANK position for 10 seconds (complete twice)

TAKE ACTION

Remind yourself that you are smart enough, bold enough, and strong enough

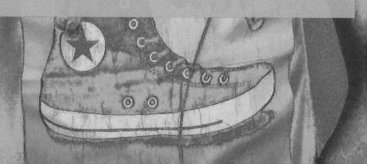

THIS WEEK'S AFFIRMATION

I AM
IMPORTANT

I Corinthians 12:14
Yes, the body has many parts, not
just one part.

YOU ARE IMPORTANT

WHAT'S ON YOUR MIND:

The values I plan to teach my children one day are the following:

_____

_____

_____

_____

EVERY DAY THIS WEEK

- Hold a PLANK position for 15 seconds (complete twice)

TAKE ACTION

Do something special for yourself every day this week

THIS WEEK'S AFFIRMATION

I AM

VALUABLE

Romans 5:8
But God showed his great love for
us by sending Christ to die for us
while we were still sinners.

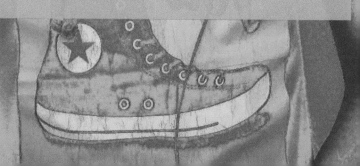

YOU ARE VALUABLE

WHAT'S ON YOUR MIND:

The best shape that describes my personality is a _____. Why?

_____

_____

_____

_____

EVERY DAY THIS WEEK

•Hold a PLANK position for 15 seconds (complete twice)

TAKE ACTION

Remind yourself this week that you have worth

THIS WEEK'S AFFIRMATION

I AM OPTIMISTIC

Jeremiah 29:11
For I know the plans I have for you, says the Lord. They are plans for good and not for evil, to give you a future and a hope.

YOU ARE OPTIMISTIC

WHAT'S ON YOUR MIND:
I am grateful for these three things.

_____

_____

_____

_____

EVERY DAY THIS WEEK
•Hold a PLANK position for 20 seconds (complete twice)

TAKE ACTION
Write down three things you hope will happen by the end of the year and post them on your mirror

THIS WEEK'S AFFIRMATION

I AM CARING

Colossians 3:12
Since you have been chosen by God who has given you this new kind of life, and because of his deep love and concern for you, you should practice tenderhearted mercy and kindness to others. Don't worry about making a good impression on them, but be ready to suffer quietly and patiently.

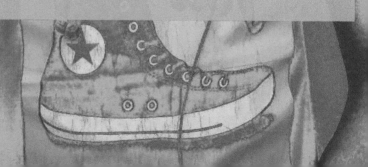

YOU ARE CARING

WHAT'S ON YOUR MIND:

My favorite part of the house is the

_____. Why?

_____

_____

_____

_____

EVERY DAY THIS WEEK

•Hold a PLANK position for 20
seconds (complete twice)

TAKE ACTION

Consider volunteering at a local
charity this weekend or later this
month

THIS WEEK'S AFFIRMATION

I AM
CONFIDENT

Psalm 27:3
Yes, though a mighty army
marches against me, my heart shall
know no fear! I am confident that
God will save me.

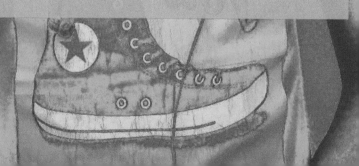

YOU ARE CONFIDENT

WHAT'S ON YOUR MIND:
Ten years from now, I will be...

_____

_____

_____

_____

EVERY DAY THIS WEEK
•*Jump rope or jump up and down for 5 minutes*

TAKE ACTION
Take a selfie that shows off your confidence

THIS WEEK'S AFFIRMATION

I AM

MOTIVATED

I Corinthians 15:58
So, my dear brothers, since future
victory is sure, be strong and steady,
always abounding in the Lord's work,
for you know that nothing you do for
the Lord is ever wasted as it would be
if there were no resurrection.

YOU ARE MOTIVATED

WHAT'S ON YOUR MIND:

The two foreign languages I would love to learn are...

_____

_____

_____

EVERY DAY THIS WEEK

•Jump rope or jump up and down for 5 minutes

TAKE ACTION

Set your alarm for 30 minutes earlier than you normally awaken and begin to pray/meditate

THIS WEEK'S AFFIRMATION

I AM FEARLESS

Isaiah 41:10
Fear not, for I am with you. Do not
be dismayed. I am your God. I will
strengthen you; I will help you; I
will uphold you with my victorious
right hand.

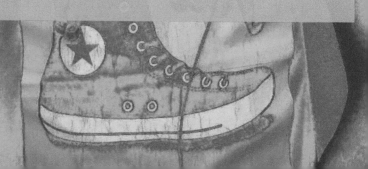

YOU ARE FEARLESS

WHAT'S ON YOUR MIND:
I cannot live without... Why?

_____

_____

_____

_____

EVERY DAY THIS WEEK
•Jump rope or jump up and down
for 5 minutes

TAKE ACTION
*Take a selfie that shows off your
most fearless facial expression*

THIS WEEK'S AFFIRMATION

I AM HEROIC

I John 4:4

Dear young friends, you belong to God and have already won your fight with those who are against Christ because there is someone in your hearts who is stronger than any evil teacher in this wicked world.

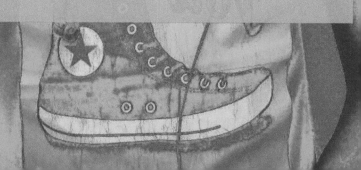

YOU ARE HEROIC

WHAT'S ON YOUR MIND:
The top five video games of all time are...

_____

_____

_____

_____

EVERY DAY THIS WEEK
•*Jump rope or jump up and down for 7 minutes*

TAKE ACTION
Write a thank you letter to a local hero and email or mail it this week

THIS WEEK'S AFFIRMATION

I AM
ADVENTURESOME

Colossians 3:23
**Work hard and cheerfully at all you
do, just as though you were
working for the Lord and not
merely for your masters**

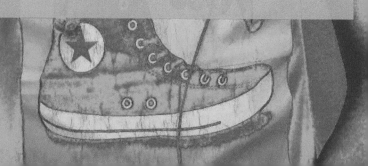

YOU ARE ADVENTURESOME

WHAT'S ON YOUR MIND:

These three words describe me perfectly...

_____

_____

_____

_____

EVERY DAY THIS WEEK

•Jump rope or jump up and down
for 7 minutes

TAKE ACTION

*Ask your parents to take you to a
local museum this week*

THIS WEEK'S AFFIRMATION

I AM
DETERMINED

Philippians 4:13
For I can do everything God asks
me to with the help of Christ who
gives me the strength and power.

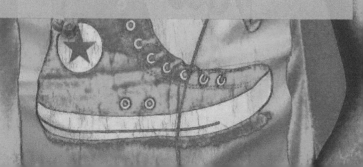

YOU ARE DETERMINED

WHAT'S ON YOUR MIND:

The toughest thing I have ever done was...

_____

_____

_____

EVERY DAY THIS WEEK

•Stretch your arms and legs for 10 minutes

TAKE ACTION

Each morning this week, wake up with a determination to accomplish something great

THIS WEEK'S AFFIRMATION

I AM HARDWORKING

Colossians 3:17
And whatever you do or say, let it be as a representative of the Lord Jesus, and come with him into the presence of God the Father to give him your thanks.

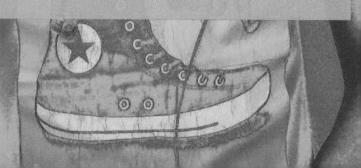

YOU ARE HARDWORKING

WHAT'S ON YOUR MIND:

The best compliment I ever received was.... Who said it?

_____

_____

_____

_____

EVERY DAY THIS WEEK

•Stretch your arms and legs for 10 minutes

TAKE ACTION

This week, help your parents complete a task around the house

THIS WEEK'S AFFIRMATION

I AM DILIGENT

2 Timothy 2:15

Work hard so God can say to you,
"Well done." Be a good workman, one
who does not need to be ashamed
when God examines your work.
Know what his Word says and means.

YOU ARE DILIGENT

WHAT'S ON YOUR MIND:

What famous person would I like to meet, one day? Why?

_____

_____

_____

_____

EVERY DAY THIS WEEK

•Take a slow 10 minute jog around the neighborhood with a friend or adult

TAKE ACTION

This week, put forth your best effort to complete every task you begin

THIS WEEK'S AFFIRMATION

I AM SUCCESSFUL

Genesis 39:2
The Lord greatly blessed Joseph there in the home of his master, so that everything he did succeeded.

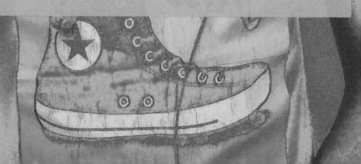

YOU ARE SUCCESSFUL

WHAT'S ON YOUR MIND:

I need to hear these three words to stay encouraged. Why?

_____

_____

_____

_____

EVERY DAY THIS WEEK

• *Take a slow 10 minute jog around the neighborhood with a friend or adult*

TAKE ACTION

Let your parents know what you accomplished this week at school

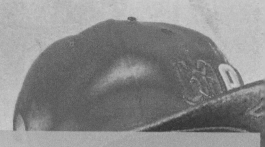

THIS WEEK'S AFFIRMATION

I AM
REMARKABLE

Psalm 139:14
Thank you for making me so
wonderfully complex! It is amazing to
think about. Your workmanship is
marvelous—and how well I know it.

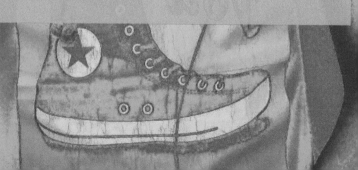

YOU ARE REMARKABLE

WHAT'S ON YOUR MIND:
The three best book I have ever read are...

_____

_____

_____

EVERY DAY THIS WEEK
•*Take a slow 15 minute jog around the neighborhood with a friend or adult*

TAKE ACTION
Take a selfie that shows off your best smile

THIS WEEK'S AFFIRMATION

I AM PATIENT

Philippians 4:6
Don't worry about anything;
instead, pray about everything; tell
God your needs, and don't forget
to thank him for his answers.

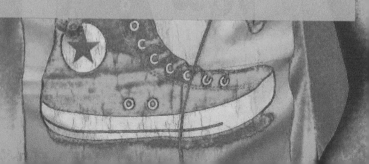

YOU ARE PATIENT

WHAT'S ON YOUR MIND:

The toughest subject in school is...

_____

_____

_____

_____

EVERY DAY THIS WEEK

•*Take a slow 15 minute jog around the neighborhood with a friend or adult*

TAKE ACTION

Exercise a little more patience this week as you interact with others

THIS WEEK'S AFFIRMATION

I AM BRAVE

Psalm 118:6

He is for me! How can I be afraid?
What can mere man do to me?

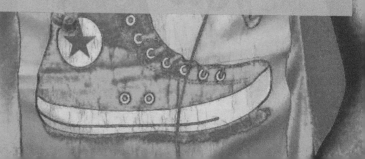

YOU ARE BRAVE

WHAT'S ON YOUR MIND:

The best advice I have ever received from my parents was...

_____

_____

_____

_____

EVERY DAY THIS WEEK

•Take a slow 20 minute jog around the neighborhood with a friend or adult

TAKE ACTION

Speak out against any wrongdoing that you witness this week

THIS WEEK'S AFFIRMATION

I AM
TRUTHFUL

Timothy 2:15

Work hard so God can say to you, "Well done." Be a good workman, one who does not need to be ashamed when God examines your work. Know what his Word says and means.

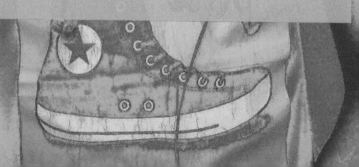

YOU ARE TRUTHFUL

WHAT'S ON YOUR MIND:

These three things upset me. Why?

_____

_____

_____

_____

EVERY DAY THIS WEEK

•Take a slow 20 minute jog around the neighborhood with a friend or adult

TAKE ACTION

Be honest when someone asks you to share your thoughts this week

THIS WEEK'S AFFIRMATION

I AM

AMBITIOUS

2 Timothy 2:22
Run from anything that gives you the
evil thoughts that young men often
have, but stay close to anything that
makes you want to do right. Have
faith and love, and enjoy the
companionship of those who love the
Lord and have pure hearts.

YOU ARE AMBITIOUS

WHAT'S ON YOUR MIND:

This is how I would spend one million dollars...

_____

_____

_____

EVERY DAY THIS WEEK

- Complete 25 pushups
- Complete 30 sit-ups
- Complete 35 jumping jacks

TAKE ACTION

Create a five-year plan that has at least three personal goals to achieve

THIS WEEK'S AFFIRMATION

I AM
IMPRESSIVE

Ephesians 2:10
It is God himself who has made us
what we are and given us new lives
from Christ Jesus; and long ages ago
he planned that we should spend
these lives in helping others.

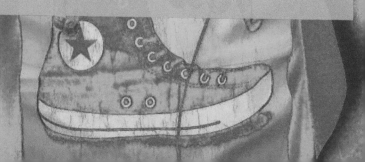

YOU ARE IMPRESSIVE

WHAT'S ON YOUR MIND:

One day, I would love to travel to...
Why?

_____

_____

_____

EVERY DAY THIS WEEK

- Complete 25 pushups
- Complete 30 sit-ups
- Complete 35 jumping jacks

TAKE ACTION

Dress up one day this week and notice how people react to you

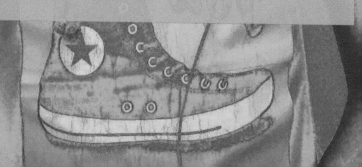

THIS WEEK'S AFFIRMATION

I AM LOYAL

Proverbs 17:17
A true friend is always loyal, and a brother is born to help in time of need.

YOU ARE LOYAL

WHAT'S ON YOUR MIND:

My hero is... Why?

_____

_____

_____

_____

EVERY DAY THIS WEEK

• Hold a PLANK position for 20 seconds (complete twice)

TAKE ACTION

Text at least three friends the affirmation for this week

THIS WEEK'S AFFIRMATION

I AM UNIQUE

I Peter 2:9
But you are not like that, for you have
been chosen by God himself—you are
priests of the King, you are holy and
pure, you are God's very own—all this
so that you may show to others how
God called you out of the darkness
into his wonderful light.

YOU ARE UNIQUE

WHAT'S ON YOUR MIND:

I could eat this food every day for the rest of my life. Why?

_____

_____

_____

_____

EVERY DAY THIS WEEK

•*Hold a PLANK position for 20 seconds (complete twice)*

TAKE ACTION

Create lyrics for an original song and post to a social media site

THIS WEEK'S AFFIRMATION

I AM CAPABLE

2 Corinthians 3:5
And not because we think we can
do anything of lasting value by
ourselves. Our only power and
success comes from God.

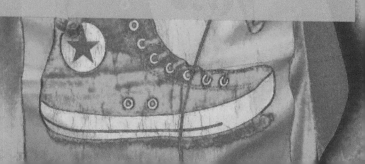

YOU ARE CAPABLE

WHAT'S ON YOUR MIND:

If I could purchase a pet, it would be a...
Why?

_____

_____

_____

_____

EVERY DAY THIS WEEK

•*Jump rope for 7 minutes*

TAKE ACTION

Challenge yourself to tackle a new hobby this week

THIS WEEK'S AFFIRMATION

I AM CREATIVE

Romans 12:6

God has given each of us the ability to do certain things well. So if God has given you the ability to prophesy, then prophesy whenever you can—as often as your faith is strong enough to receive a message from God.

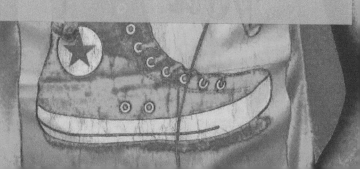

YOU ARE CREATIVE

WHAT'S ON YOUR MIND:

The best way to handle a bully is...

_____

_____

_____

_____

EVERY DAY THIS WEEK

•Jump rope for 7 minutes

TAKE ACTION

Take a photo of something you created on your own

THIS WEEK'S AFFIRMATION

I AM SMART

Proverbs 2:6
For the Lord grants wisdom! His every word is a treasure of knowledge and understanding.

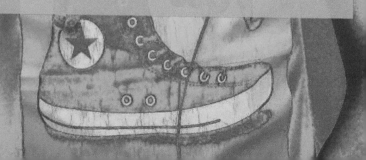

YOU ARE SMART

WHAT'S ON YOUR MIND:
The best sport's team is... Because?

_____

_____

_____

EVERY DAY THIS WEEK
•Take a jog around the neighborhood for 20 minutes with a friend or adult

TAKE ACTION
Develop a solution to a problem in your school and submit it to the principal

THIS WEEK'S AFFIRMATION

I AM

BRILLIANT

2 Peter 1:5 - But to obtain these gifts, you need more than faith; you must also work hard to be good, and even that is not enough. For then you must learn to know God better and discover what he wants you to do.

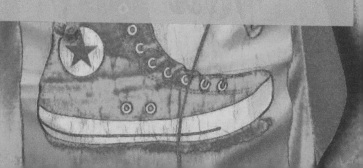

YOU ARE BRILLIANT

WHAT'S ON YOUR MIND:
The best way to spend the weekend is...

_____

_____

_____

_____

EVERY DAY THIS WEEK
•Take a jog around the neighborhood for 20 minutes with a friend or adult

TAKE ACTION
Develop a plan that solves an issue in your community and present it to the local news station

THIS WEEK'S AFFIRMATION

I AM
TALENTED

Ephesians 2:10
It is God himself who has made us
what we are and given us new lives
from Christ Jesus; and long ages ago
he planned that we should spend
these lives in helping others.

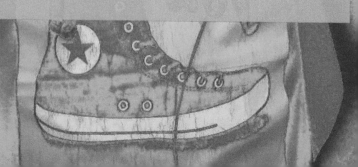

YOU ARE TALENTED

WHAT'S ON YOUR MIND:
What do you wish that you could change about the world in which you live?

_____
_____
_____

EVERY DAY THIS WEEK
•Take a 30 minute walk around the neighborhood with a friend or adult

TAKE ACTION
Make a video that displays your best talent

THIS WEEK'S AFFIRMATION

I AM GENUINE

I Timothy 1:5
What I am eager for is that all the Christians there will be filled with love that comes from pure hearts, and that their minds will be clean and their faith strong.

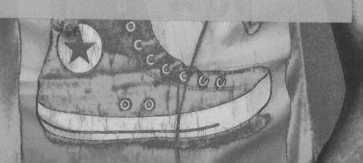

YOU ARE GENUINE

WHAT'S ON YOUR MIND:

The peer pressures that are difficult to resist are...

_____

_____

_____

EVERY DAY THIS WEEK

•Take a 30 minute walk around the neighborhood with a friend or adult

TAKE ACTION

Compliment your favorite teacher, this week

THIS WEEK'S AFFIRMATION

I AM GIFTED

I Peter 4:10
God has given each of you some
special abilities; be sure to use them to
help each other, passing on to others
God's many kinds of blessings.

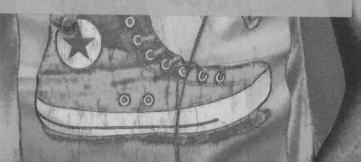

YOU ARE GIFTED

WHAT'S ON YOUR MIND:

If I had one super human power, it would be the ability to...

_____

_____

_____

EVERY DAY THIS WEEK

- Complete 10 Burpees
- Complete 15 squats
- Complete 20 mountain climbers

TAKE ACTION

Create something from using a piece of paper, some tape, and a marker

THIS WEEK'S AFFIRMATION

I AM
RESPONSIBLE

Proverbs 10:9
A good man has firm footing, but a
crook will slip and fall.

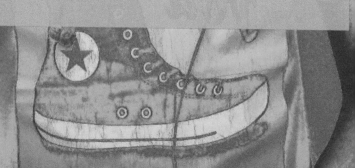

YOU ARE RESPONSIBLE

WHAT'S ON YOUR MIND:
These three things make me angry...

_____

_____

_____

_____

EVERY DAY THIS WEEK
- Complete 10 Burpees
- Complete 15 squats
- Complete 20 mountain climbers

TAKE ACTION
Complete a chore around the house before being asked to do it

THIS WEEK'S AFFIRMATION

I AM COOPERATIVE

Luke 6:31
Treat others as you want them to treat you.

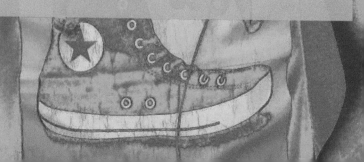

YOU ARE COOPERATIVE

WHAT'S ON YOUR MIND:

My favorite teacher is... Why?

_____
_____
_____
_____

EVERY DAY THIS WEEK

- Complete 10 Burpees
- Complete 15 squats
- Complete 20 mountain climbers

TAKE ACTION

Text your best friend the affirmation for this week

THIS WEEK'S AFFIRMATION

I AM
DEVOTED

Matthew 6:24
You cannot serve two masters: God
and money. For you will hate one and
love the other, or else the other way
around.

YOU ARE DEVOTED

WHAT'S ON YOUR MIND:

How important is my family to me?
Why?

_____

_____

_____

EVERY DAY THIS WEEK

- *Complete 15 burpees*
- *Complete 20 squats*
- *Complete 25 mountain climbers*

TAKE ACTION

Read a Bible verse every night for
one week

THIS WEEK'S AFFIRMATION

I AM
COMPETITIVE

I Corinthians 9:24
In a race everyone runs, but only
one person gets first prize. So run
your race to win.

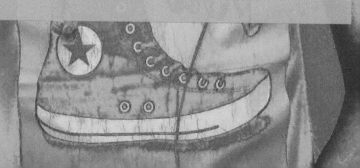

YOU ARE COMPETITIVE

WHAT'S ON YOUR MIND:

The most embarrassing moment in my life happened when I...

_____

_____

_____

EVERY DAY THIS WEEK

- Complete 15 burpees
- Complete 20 squats
- Complete 25 mountain climbers

TAKE ACTION

Challenge a friend to a game of Uno or board game of your choice

THIS WEEK'S AFFIRMATION

I AM SINCERE

I John 3:18
Little children, let us stop just saying
we love people; let us really love
them, and show it by our actions.

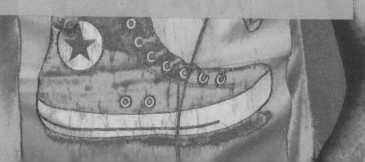

YOU ARE SINCERE

WHAT'S ON YOUR MIND:
The three things I worry about are...

_____

_____

_____

EVERY DAY THIS WEEK
- Complete 5 pushups
- Complete 10 sit-ups
- Complete 20 jumping jacks

TAKE ACTION
Give someone in your family a big morning hug

THIS WEEK'S AFFIRMATION

I AM
INNOVATIVE

Psalm 96:1
Sing a new song to the Lord! Sing it
everywhere around the world!

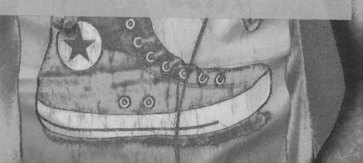

YOU ARE INNOVATIVE

WHAT'S ON YOUR MIND:

What is my most memorable vacation?
What made it so special?

_____
_____
_____

EVERY DAY THIS WEEK
- Complete 5 pushups
- Complete 10 sit-ups
- Complete 20 jumping jacks

TAKE ACTION
Call a friend or relative you have not
spoken to in a while

THIS WEEK'S AFFIRMATION

I AM
COOPERATIVE

Luke 6:31
And as you wish that others would
do to you, do so to them.

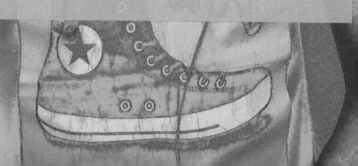

YOU ARE COOPERATIVE

WHAT'S ON YOUR MIND:

These five players would make up the best sports team, ever! Because...

_____

_____

_____

_____

EVERY DAY THIS WEEK
- *Complete 7 pushups*
- *Complete 15 sit-ups*
- *Complete 25 jumping jacks*

TAKE ACTION

Volunteer to assist someone with a task at school

THIS WEEK'S AFFIRMATION

I AM
FRIENDLY

Psalm 133:1
How wonderful it is, how pleasant,
when brothers live in harmony!

YOU ARE FRIENDLY

WHAT'S ON YOUR MIND:

These three things make me laugh out loud?

_____

_____

_____

_____

EVERY DAY THIS WEEK

- *Complete 10 pushups*
- *Complete 15 sit-ups*
- *Complete 25 jumping jacks*

TAKE ACTION

This week, go out of your way to be friendly towards others

THIS WEEK'S AFFIRMATION

I AM
AUTHENTIC

Genesis 1:27
So God made man like his Maker.
Like God did God make man; Man
and maid did he make them.

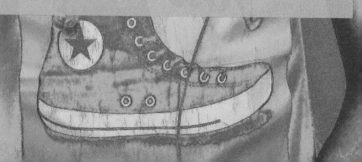

YOU ARE AUTHENTIC

WHAT'S ON YOUR MIND:

My most memorable day at school occurred on... What happened?

_____

_____

_____

_____

EVERY DAY THIS WEEK

- Complete 5 pushups
- Complete 10 sit-ups
- Complete 20 jumping jacks

TAKE ACTION

Create an original drawing and share with family and friends

THIS WEEK'S AFFIRMATION

I AM
ASPIRING

Exodus 20:12
Honor your father and mother, that
you may have a long, good life in the
land the Lord your God will give you.

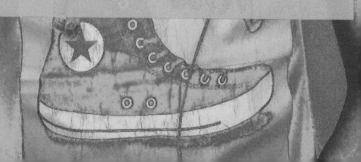

YOU ARE ASPIRING

WHAT'S ON YOUR MIND:

Who is God to me?

_____

_____

_____

_____

EVERY DAY THIS WEEK
- Complete 15 pushups
- Complete 20 sit-ups
- Complete 30 jumping jacks

TAKE ACTION
Cut out a picture of what you would like to become and tape it to your bedroom mirror

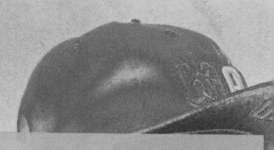

THIS WEEK'S AFFIRMATION

I AM
FOCUSED

Colossians 3:2
Let heaven fill your thoughts; don't
spend your time worrying about
things down here.

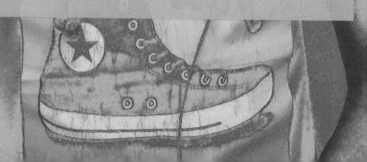

YOU ARE FOCUSED

WHAT'S ON YOUR MIND:

What are the major things that distract my attention?

_____

_____

_____

EVERY DAY THIS WEEK

- *Complete 15 pushups*
- *Complete 20 sit-ups*
- *Complete 30 jumping jacks*

TAKE ACTION

Write down your top three goals for the year and post them next to your bed

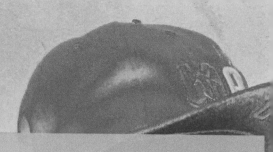

THIS WEEK'S AFFIRMATION

I AM

CHARITABLE

Acts 20:35

And I was a constant example to you in helping the poor; for I remembered the words of the Lord Jesus, "It is more blessed to give than to receive."

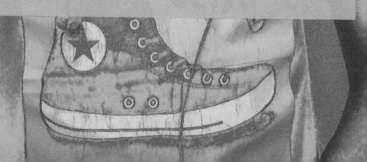

YOU ARE CHARITABLE

WHAT'S ON YOUR MIND:

Why is it important to help those who are in need?

_____

_____

_____

_____

EVERY DAY THIS WEEK
- Complete 20 pushups
- Complete 25 sit-ups
- Complete 35 jumping jacks

TAKE ACTION
Complete three (3) acts of kindness by the end of the week

Ingram Content Group UK Ltd.
Milton Keynes UK
UKHW020952130623
423367UK00005B/12